Valentine's Day

TIP

YOU NEED:

Carnival

TIP
YOU NEED:

Easter

Cut out the pictures on page 9 too.

TIP
YOU NEED:

Easter

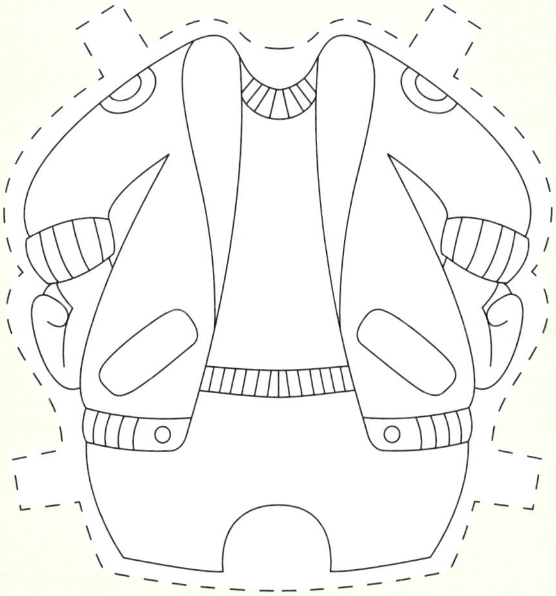

TIP
YOU NEED:

Mother's Day

TIP
YOU NEED:

June Festival

TIP
YOU NEED:

Father's Day

TIP
YOU NEED:

Halloween

TIP
YOU NEED:

Thanksgiving

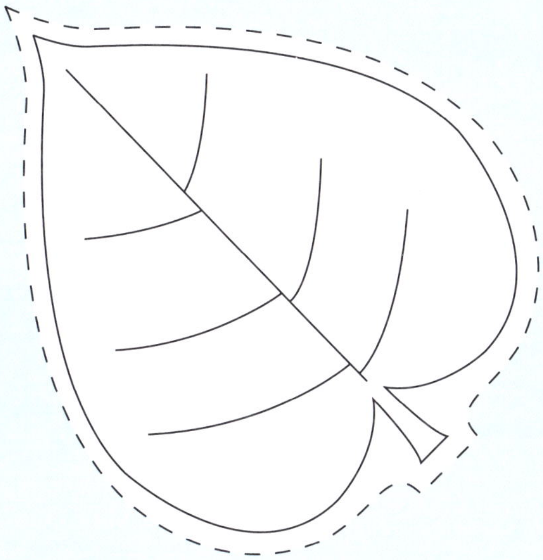

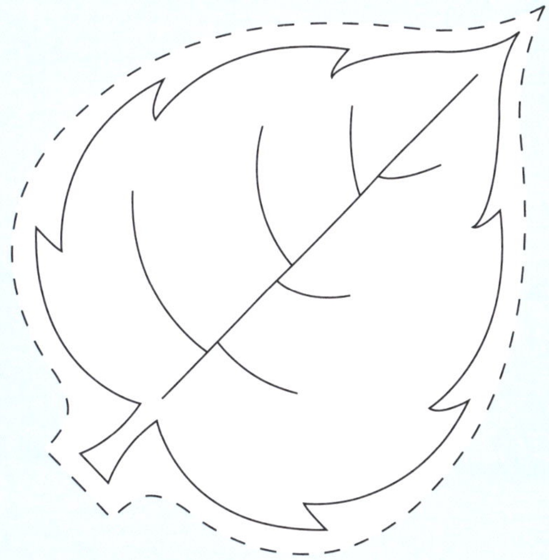

TIP
YOU NEED:

Christmas

TIP
YOU NEED: